Contents

A **pull-out answers section** (pages A1 to A8) appears in the centre of this book, between pages 20 and 21. It also gives simple guidance on how best to use this book. Remove this section before you begin working through the tests.

⬇ ■ Underline the **two** words, one from each group, that are most **similar** in meaning.

> **Example** (<u>anger</u>, sadden, cross)   (<u>enrage</u>, grow, cry)

1. (reject, robust, yield)   (surrender, reluctant, roam)
2. (adversity, mystery, trickery)   (gravity, misfortune, symmetry)
3. (rotund, greedy, malicious)   (appeal, nutritious, avaricious)
4. (tranquillity, simplicity, audacity)   (improvement, indent, impudence)
5. (icon, acorn, eminent)   (bland, famous, signal)

■ In each of the sentences below, the word in capitals has three letters missing. Those three letters spell a word. Write the three-letter word on the line.

> **Example** He was much **TER** than his younger brother.   <u>ALL</u>   (TALLER)

6. Their mum woke up the **EARST**. _____
7. She made several **ORS** in her spelling test. _____
8. It was a long **JNEY** to get home. _____
9. The girl felt really **MISBLE** when she heard the bad news. _____
10. He always **EAVOURS** to finish his work on time. _____

■ Find the missing number in each sequence and write it on the line.

> **Example** 7   14   <u>21</u>   28   35   42   (+7 each time)

11. 24   12   6   3   _____   0.75   13. 2   4   6   10   16   _____
12. 145   220   295   370   445   _____   14. 16   25   36   _____   64   81

■ Work out the answers. Write your answers on the lines.

15. There are 15 pupils in a class. Of these children, 4 have blonde hair and 6 have brown hair. The number of children who have red hair is half the number of blondes, and the rest have black hair. How many children do not have red hair? _____

16. Daniel is inviting some people to his birthday party. He invites 7 friends from his class, 4 from his old school and 8 from his swimming club. The rest of the guests are his neighbours. There are a total of 25 people at his party, including him and his parents. How many people at the party are not from his class? _____

End of test.

Score:		Time taken:		Target met?	

Target time: **10 minutes**

■ Find the missing number in each of these equations and write it on the line.

Example 20 – 5 = 12 + ___3___

1. 79 + 2 = 9 × _____
2. 800 ÷ 100 = 2 × _____
3. 410 – 10 = 10 × _____
4. (56 × 10) + 50 = (70 × 9) – _____
5. 50 × 11 = (57 × 10) – _____

■ Underline the **two** words, one from each group, that are most **opposite** in meaning.

Example (friendly, <u>enemy</u>, silent)   (<u>ally</u>, kind, whisper)

6. (gaunt, sly, hollow)   (obese, cunning, gallant)
7. (eventual, frequency, frequent)   (celebratory, ocular, occasional)
8. (sum, estimate, divide)   (answer, calculate, circulate)
9. (questionable, important, quizzical)   (trivial, famed, powerful)
10. (transparent, trinket, optional)   (oblong, stampede, opaque)

■ Match the number codes to the words. One code is missing. Use this to help you work out the answers to the questions. Write your answers on the lines.

FIND   MEET   MIND   TIME   4182   6182   6779

What is the code for:

11. **FEET**? _____   12. **TIE**? _____   13. **DIME**? _____
14. What does the code **6187** mean? _____

■ Work out the answers. Write your answers on the lines.

15. Demi has a £10 note. She spends £7.79 on groceries and 85p on a bus ticket home. How much money does Demi have left? _____

16. Kris has 42 cupcakes. 12 are chocolate. There are twice as many vanilla cakes as there are chocolate. The rest of the cakes are lemon. How many lemon cakes does Kris have? _____

End of test.

Score:		Time taken:		Target met?	

■ Underline the two words, **one** from each group, that best complete the sentence.

Example **Earth** is to (mud, dirty, <u>planet</u>) as **cow** is to (field, <u>mammal</u>, bull).

1. **Joyful** is to (clown, elated, miserable) as **jealous** is to (envious, anxious, cross).
2. **Conclude** is to (terminate, commence, eliminate) as **pursue** is to (defy, chase, irritate).
3. **Understand** is to (listen, comprehend, instruction) as **delete** is to (omit, erase, undermine).
4. **Reasonable** is to (intellectual, persuasive, illogical) as **general** is to (specific, determine, select).
5. **Calculation** is to (computer, numeracy, exact) as **estimation** is to (imprecise, illegible, brain).

■ Use the information given to answer each sum. Write your answer as a **letter**.

Example $A = 10$ $B = 6$ $C = 3$ $D = 12$ $E = 18$ **$B \times C =$** ___E___   ($6 \times 3 = 18$)

6. $A = 14$ $B = 36$ $C = 56$ $D = 9$ $E = 63$ **$C \div A \times D =$** _____
7. $A = 4200$ $B = 12$ $C = 720$ $D = 640$ $E = 70$ **$A \div E \times B =$** _____
8. $A = 2.3$ $B = 0.6$ $C = 3$ $D = 0.5$ $E = 1.9$ **$B \times C + D =$** _____
9. $A = 3$ $B = 19$ $C = 35$ $D = 8$ $E = 45$ **$D^2 - B =$** _____
10. $A = 21$ $B = 42$ $C = 17$ $D = 207$ $E = 34$ **$\frac{E}{C} \times A =$** _____

■ Find the missing letters in each sequence and write them on the line. Use the alphabet to help you.

A B C D E F G H I J K L M N O P Q R S T U V W X Y Z

Example Hi   Jk   Lm   No   ___Pq___
(first letter +2 capitals; second letter +2 lower case)

11. BX   FB   JF   _____

13. GC   DD   AE   _____   UG

12. AH   YF   WD   _____   SZ

14. KE   IG   _____   EK   CM

■ Work out the answers. Write your answers on the lines.

15. In 1 minute, Sasha takes **43** steps. It takes him **301** steps to travel from his house to the shops. If he leaves home at **10:24**, at what time will he reach the shops if he walks steadily? _____

16. Janine likes to sleep for **9** hours and **45** minutes every night. On Monday she needs to be awake at **7.25 a.m.** What time should she go to bed on Sunday to get as much sleep as she would like?

_____

End of test.

Score:		Time taken:		Target met?	

Target time: 10 minutes

■ Underline the pair of words that are most **opposite** in meaning.

Example (lift, drop)   (snow, wind)   (listen, learn)

1. (desperate, disparate)   (intricate, detailed)   (smart, slovenly)
2. (spendthrift, miser)   (splinter, prison)   (cell, master)
3. (around, about)   (wax, wane)   (during, while)
4. (heroic, infancy)   (superior, inferior)   (admiral, officer)
5. (material, fabric)   (servile, servant)   (automatic, manual)

■ Find **one** missing letter that completes **both** pairs of words. Write it on the lines.

Example strea [m] ile   doo [m] arry

6. elop [__] go   grap [__] very
7. acqui [__] alon   fein [__] wice
8. equi [__] arent   trum [__] earl
9. squea [__] arge   snar [__] urk
10. concer [__] ext   spou [__] rout

■ Using the alphabet to help you, find the letter pair that completes each sentence. Write it on the line.

A B C D E F G H I J K L M N O P Q R S T U V W X Y Z

Example **FG** is to **EF** as **LM** is to ___KL___.   (–1, –1)

11. **VE** is to **YA** as **KH** is to _____.
12. **DY** is to **XT** as **FJ** is to _____.
13. **JV** is to **QE** as **KU** is to _____.
14. **GR** is to **NP** as **IL** is to _____.

■ Circle the letter next to the **true** statement for each question.

15. Igneous rocks are formed when lava cools down. Basalt is an igneous rock.

   If the above statements are true, which one of the following statements must also be true?
   A. Lava comes from volcanoes.
   B. Basalt is hot.
   C. Basalt can be ignited.
   D. Basalt is formed from cooled lava.

16. The Milky Way is a spiral galaxy. Saturn is a planet in the Milky Way.

   If the above statements are true, which one of the following statements must also be true?
   A. Saturn is part of a spiral galaxy.
   B. Saturn has rings around it made of debris.
   C. Astronomers study spiral galaxies.
   D. Jupiter is next to Saturn.

   End of test.

Score:	Time taken:	Target met?

Section 1 Test 5

■ Find the **four-letter word** hidden across two or more consecutive words in each sentence below. The order of the letters must stay the same. Underline the word and write it on the line.

> **Example** I like lots <u>of tr</u>eacle on my porridge! ____soft____

1. My uncle favours chocolate cake over salad! _____
2. The drummer's cymbal makes an awfully loud noise. _____
3. I could not help him as I was myself on dangerous ground. _____
4. When I asked if you would like a gold medal I meant that you had won the race! _____
5. The wasp continued to hover beside the cake. _____

■ Underline the **two** words in each row that contain all the **same** letters.

> **Example** <u>angel</u>   gland   ankle   <u>glean</u>   gleam

6. beaks   baker   bleak   brave   break   9. bores   bloat   robes   broad   boast
7. blare   brain   beard   burnt   bared   10. rules   uncle   clues   cruel   ulcer
8. being   bring   begin   brain   bench

■ Work out the missing numbers. Write them on the lines.

> **Example** 11 [88] 8   9 [54] 6   15 [___45___] 3
> (a × b = ?, where a represents the number on the left and b represents the number on the right)

11. 3 [26] 10   5 [20] 5   2 [_____] 2   13. 17 [64] 15   36 [72] 0   54 [_____] 6
12. 125 [150] 100   9 [10] 8   5 [_____] 1   14. 5 [34] 12   10 [88] 34   29 [_____] 11

■ Work out the answers. Write your answers on the lines.

15. I am going on holiday on 19 September. I will spend a day travelling to France. Then I will spend 2 days in France, after which I will spend a day travelling to Germany. I will spend 4 days in Germany, and then will spend 2 days travelling to England. On what date do I arrive in England?

_____

16. It was my 11th birthday 248 days ago. If it is not a leap year, how many days is it until my next birthday? _____

End of test.

Score:		Time taken:		Target met?	

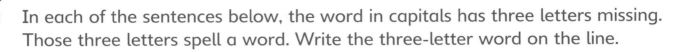

Target time: 10 minutes

⬇
■ In each of the sentences below, the word in capitals has three letters missing. Those three letters spell a word. Write the three-letter word on the line.

> **Example** He was much **TER** than his younger brother. ___ALL___ (TALLER)

1. The vase was **PRLESS**. _____
2. The model broke because it was not very **ROT**. _____
3. The champion boxer remained **UNBEN**. _____
4. I opened the door to the **RESICE** of my aunt. _____
5. The naughty boy was punished **SRELY** by his mother. _____

■ Underline the **two** words, one from each group, that together make one new word. The word from the first group comes first.

> **Example** (<u>tea</u>, coffee, cream)   (drink, <u>room</u>, milk)   (tearoom)

6. (night, dusk, sun)   (party, star, gown)
7. (old, new, brand)   (sprint, run, paper)
8. (lake, her, fish)   (ring, diamond, jewel)
9. (night, rodent, bat)   (he, us, person)
10. (hurt, scar, body)   (rush, let, buy)

■ Find the missing number in each of these equations and write it on the line.

> **Example** $20 - 5 = 12 +$ ___3___

11. $(170 \div 10) \times 3 = 204 \div$ _____
12. $(70 + 50) \times 2 = 300 -$ _____
13. $10^2 + 12^2 = 245 -$ _____
14. $3^3 \times 5^2 = 200 + 150 +$ _____

■ Circle the letter next to the **true** statement for each question.

15. Meteorology is the study of the atmosphere. Cloud formations are part of the atmosphere.

   If the above statements are true, which one of the following statements must also be true?
   A. Another name for rain is precipitation.
   B. Meteorologists study the formation of clouds.
   C. High pressure leads to warm weather.
   D. Clouds are always white or grey.

16. Creatures which can live in and out of water are called amphibians. Frogs live in and out of water.

   If the above statements are true, which one of the following statements must also be true?
   A. Frogs are the same as toads.
   B. Frogs live beside ponds.
   C. Frogs eat flies.
   D. Frogs are amphibians.

End of test.

Score:	Time taken:	Target met?

■ If these words were listed in alphabetical order, which word would come **third**? Write the answer on the line.

Example alert   ample   handle   hinder   ankle   <u>ankle</u>

1. harmonica   harmony   harp   harass   heaven   _____

2. leather   lethargy   liable   lentil   lethal   _____

3. wander   wonder   wondrous   window   wicked   _____

4. drab   dreary   derail   dread   drier   _____

5. caution   capsule   cautious   capital   capture   _____

■ In each group, three words go together and two are the odd ones out. Underline the two words that do **not** go with the other three.

Example <u>define</u>   certain   sure   <u>give</u>   definite

6. cymbal   bassoon   oboe   clarinet   cello

7. glockenspiel   harpsichord   piano   xylophone   chime bar

8. grotto   glade   cave   cavern   oasis

9. enrage   calm   placate   infuriate   exasperate

10. deform   renovate   refurbish   deface   disfigure

■ Underline the **two** words, one from each group, that together make one new word. The word from the first group comes first.

Example (<u>tea</u>, coffee, cream)   (drink, <u>room</u>, milk)   (tearoom)

11. (miss, left, right)   (out, take, over)

12. (on, in, at)   (sign, risk, vest)

13. (building, out, over)   (site, light, burst)

14. (sub, buck, rain)   (dew, doe, due)

■ Work out the answers. Write your answers on the lines.

15. There are 12 string instrument players and 14 brass instrument players in the school orchestra. Half the brass players play the trumpet and 3 of them play the horn. There are 2 drummers. How many people are there in the orchestra? _____

16. Nadya is organising a fashion show. Jamie, Alice, Susie and Li are modelling the outfits. Each wears 4 different outfits. All of Li's outfits are pink. Half of Alice's outfits are pink and the rest are red. One of Jamie's outfits is red; the others are blue. Susie wears 2 outfits with pink sequins on and the other 2 are plain white. How many outfits do **not** have pink on them? _____   End of test.

Score:		Time taken:		Target met?	

Target time: **10 minutes**

■ Underline the **two** words, one from each group, that are most **similar** in meaning.

> **Example** (<u>anger</u>, sadden, cross)   (<u>enrage</u>, grow, cry)

1. (steel, steal, iron)   (platinum, crease, purloin)
2. (mandate, malady, hollow)   (masseur, illness, bellow)
3. (encircle, rectangular, shape)   (surround, dimension, square)
4. (precarious, graceful, physical)   (elongate, elaborate, elegant)
5. (courteous, illegible, ignorant)   (lawful, criminal, polite)

■ Change the first word into the last word. Only change **one** letter at a time, making two new four-letter words in the middle.

> **Example** GILT [_SILT_][_SALT_] MALT

6. RACE [_____][_____] HIDE
7. TRIP [_____][_____] PRAM
8. BOOK [_____][_____] LOCH
9. TEND [_____][_____] MEAL
10. SAND [_____][_____] HINT

■ Using the alphabet to help you, crack the code. Write the answer on the line.

A B C D E F G H I J K L M N O P Q R S T U V W X Y Z

> **Example** If the code for **SIT** is **TJU**, what is the code for **SAT**? _TBU_
>
> (+ 1 from the word to the code)

11. If the code for **HEADPHONES** is **IFBEQIPOFT**, what is **MUSICAL** in code? _____
12. If the code for **COATHANGER** is **EQCVJCPIGT**, what is **CURTAINS** in code? _____
13. If the code **RVFTUJPO** means **QUESTION**, what does the code **BOTXFS** mean? _____
14. If **EYELASH** is written in code as **ICIPEWL**, what is the code for **EYEBROW**? _____

■ Work out the answers. Write your answers on the lines.

15. Michelle is meeting her friend Melissa at **3.05 p.m.** If she drove without stopping it would take her **34 minutes** to travel to their meeting point. However, Michelle needs to stop for petrol on her way there. It will take her **5 minutes** to fill her car with petrol and another **6 minutes** to pay. What time should Michelle leave to be on time to meet Melissa? _____

16. How many minutes are there in **2.5 hours**? _____

End of test.

Score:		Time taken:		Target met?	

■ Underline the word in the first group that goes best with the words in brackets.

Example <u>blue</u>, red, orange   (turquoise, navy, cyan)

1. postcard, telescope, vowel   (text, email, letter)
2. visit, hammer, measure   (anvil, mallet, saw)
3. tarragon, flagon, decagon   (octagon, hexagon, heptagon)
4. spend, blossom, spurn   (flourish, thrive, prosper)
5. saunter, sprint, row   (amble, stroll, meander)

■ Find the missing number in each of these equations and write it on the line.

Example $20 - 5 = 12 +$ ___3___

6. $130 \times 20 = 50^2 +$ _____
7. $40 + 30 - 75 = 15 -$ _____
8. $150 \times 50 = 10\,000 -$ _____

9. $20^2 + 20^3 = 4200 \times$ _____
10. $(15 \times 5) \div 2 = 35 +$ _____

■ Find the missing letters in each sequence and write them on the line. Use the alphabet to help you.

A B C D E F G H I J K L M N O P Q R S T U V W X Y Z

Example Hi   Jk   Lm   No   ___Pq___
(first letter +2 capitals; second letter +2 lower case)

11. BC   CD   DE   _____   FG
12. HH   HP   HX   HF   _____

13. PP   OQ   MS   JV   _____
14. ZP   PZ   GI   YQ   _____

■ Work out the answers. Write your answers on the lines.

15. There are 6 flavours of ice-cream to choose from: chocolate, strawberry, mint, vanilla, hazelnut and orange. Betty orders 3 scoops of chocolate, mint and vanilla. Tam has the same as Betty with an extra scoop of orange. Kieran has orange and chocolate but is allergic to hazelnuts. Lucia orders all the flavours except mint. Which ice-cream flavour do they **all** order? _____

16. Selma and Imo are going to university. Between them they have 4 blue suitcases, 2 red suitcases and 3 brown suitcases. The brown suitcases are small; the rest are large. Each of their cars can hold 2 big suitcases and 1 small suitcase. How many cars do they need to fit in all their suitcases?

_____

End of test.

Score:		Time taken:		Target met?	

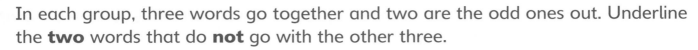

Target time: 10 minutes

■ In each group, three words go together and two are the odd ones out. Underline the **two** words that do **not** go with the other three.

> **Example** <u>define</u>   certain   sure   <u>give</u>   definite

1. lone   extrovert   solitary   single   social
2. consider   deliberate   assess   intend   mistake
3. convene   scatter   gather   disperse   assemble
4. polite   juice   cordial   rude   civil
5. ancient   abbreviate   archaic   brief   antique

■ In each of the sentences below, the word in capitals has three letters missing. Those three letters spell a word. Write the three-letter word on the line.

> **Example** He was much **TER** than his younger brother.   <u>ALL</u>   (TALLER)

6. The hermit lived in **SOUDE**. _____
7. The detective thought the fingerprints were a **SIGNIFIT** clue. _____
8. The millionaire **SQUERED** his riches. _____
9. The enemy **SURRERED** after a long battle. _____
10. Our teacher put me and my friend in **SEATE** groups. _____

■ Using the alphabet to help you, crack the code. Write the answer on the line.
A B C D E F G H I J K L M N O P Q R S T U V W X Y Z

> **Example** If the code for **SIT** is **TJU**, what is the code for **SAT**?   <u>TBU</u>
>
> (+ 1 from the word to the code)

11. If the code for **UMBRELLA** is **FNYIVOOZ**, what is **RAINFALL** in code? _____
12. If the code **JCMNYPB** means **LEOPARD**, what does **RGECP** mean? _____
13. If the code **NQZMFD** means **ORANGE**, what does **RBZQKDS** mean? _____
14. If **GRASS** is written in code as **HRBST**, what is the code for **LAWN**? _____

■ Use the word's definition to help you fill in the missing letters.

15. TH __ __ G __ TF __ __   considerate, pensive, attentive
16. AD __ __ N __ AG __   benefit, gain, "pro"

End of test.

Score:		Time taken:		Target met?	

■ Move one letter from the first word to the second word to make two new words. Write the two new words on the lines.

> **Example** trip, star _____rip_____, ____start____ (move the **t**)

1. ideal, beach _____, _____

2. cable, lanes _____, _____

3. pamper, other _____, _____

4. brought, bawl _____, _____

5. shingle, boot _____, _____

■ Use the information given to answer each sum. Write your answer as a **letter**.

> **Example** A = 10   B = 6   C = 3   D = 12   E = 18   **B × C =** __E__ (6 × 3 = 18)

6. A = 9   B = 6   C = 12   D = 144   E = 2   **D ÷ E ÷ B =** _____

7. A = 9   B = –5   C = –8   D = 2   E = 12   **B + A – E =** _____

8. A = 120   B = 50   C = 108   D = 600   E = 115   **D ÷ B + C =** _____

9. A = 2   B = 1   C = 3   D = 4   E = 8 $\frac{B}{A} + \frac{A}{D} =$ _____

10. A = 37   B = 15   C = 5   D = 27   E = 9   **E × B ÷ C =** _____

■ The word in square brackets has been made by some of the letters from the two outside words. Make a new word in the middle of the second group of words in the same way. Write the new word on the line.

> **Example** (help [hear] pair)   (soup [__sort__] grit)

11. (late [tail] list)   (lean [_____] warm)   13. (play [pile] live)   (mind [_____] lane)

12. (sign [sing] rain)   (reek [_____] loop)   14. (grain [bring] begin)   (rouse [_____] lords)

■ Work out the answers. Write your answers on the lines.

15. It takes Ling **45** minutes to do her homework and **50** minutes to do her chores. She wants to watch a television programme that starts at **7.15** p.m. What time must Ling start doing her homework and chores if she wants to be finished **5** minutes before her programme begins? _____

16. Grace is **27**. Her daughter is one-third of her age and her son is one-third of her daughter's age. How old is her son? _____

End of test.

Score: _____   Time taken: _____   Target met? _____

Target time: 10 minutes

■ Underline the word in brackets that is most **opposite** in meaning to the word in capitals.

Example LOUD   (noisy, <u>quiet</u>, shout, roar)

1. ANCESTOR   (dependent, traitor, descendant, dissent)
2. STATIONARY   (valuable, futile, mobile, pencil)
3. SHORTAGE   (surmise, surplus, lengthy, tallest)
4. AGGRESSIVE   (acquire, amiable, ferocious, angry)
5. ALTITUDE   (depth, mountainous, alternative, peak)

■ Find **one** missing letter that completes **both** pairs of words. Write it on the lines.

Example strea [_m_] ile   doo [_m_] arry

6. frot [__] angar   boot [__] aughty
7. cape [__] iddle   caree [__] evel
8. thrif [__] epid   flaun [__] alent

9. braw [__] avy   iro [__] iece
10. com [__] arley   tom [__] reach

■ Using the alphabet to help you, crack the code. Write the answer on the line.

A B C D E F G H I J K L M N O P Q R S T U V W X Y Z

Example If the code for **SIT** is **TJU**, what is the code for **SAT**?   TBU
(+1 from the word to the code)

11. If **ALPHABET** is written in code as **ZOKSZYVG**, what is the code for **EXAMINATION**? _____

12. If the code **XSJOLMF** means **WRINKLE**, what does the code **NPJTUVSF** mean? _____

13. If **SUNGLASSES** is written in code as **HFMTOZHHVH**, what is the code for **EXPRESSION**? _____

14. If the code for **STOPWATCH** is **TVRTBGAKQ**, what is the code for **TIMER**? _____

■ Work out the answers. Write your answers on the lines.

15. There are 35 people on a bus. At the first bus stop, 12 people leave the bus and 5 get on. At the next stop, 11 people leave and 14 get on. How many people are now on the bus? _____

16. Ali leaves for work at 8.20 a.m. It takes him 35 minutes to get to work. He has lunch 3 hours and 40 minutes later. What time does he have lunch? _____

End of test.

Score:	Time taken:	Target met?

■ Find the missing number in each sequence and write it on the line.

| **Example** 7 14 _21_ 28 35 42 (+7 each time) |

1. 510   530   550   570   590   _____
2. 888   88.8   8.88   _____   0.0888
3. 16   32   64   128   _____   512

4. 17   18   9   10   _____   6   3
5. 56   28   14   7   _____

....

■ Underline the **two** words, one from each group, that together make one new word. The word from the first group comes first.

| **Example** (tea, coffee, cream)   (drink, room, milk)   (tearoom) |

6. (find, feed, cater)   (house, pillar, structure)
7. (change, alter, new)   (native, own, equal)
8. (dirt, germ, cell)   (inate, proper, primal)

9. (family, aunt, relation)   (boat, ship, harbour)
10. (kit, bag, army)   (ten, twelve, organise)

....

■ Match the number codes to the words. One code is missing. Use these to help you work out the answers to the questions. Write your answers on the lines.

TOMB   BOAT   COMB   MOAT   3487   7436   2436

What is the code for:

11. **ATOM**? _____   12. **TABOO**? _____   13. **COMMA**? _____
14. What does the code **34774** mean? _____

....

■ Circle the letter next to the **true** statement for each question.

15. Porcelain is a special type of clay used to make china objects. Gran's teapot is made from porcelain.

If the above statements are true, which one of the following statements must also be true?
A. Clay is a type of china.
B. Porcelain is expensive.
C. Gran's teapot is made from special clay.
D. Gran has china teacups.

16. Scandinavia is in the northern part of Europe. Scandinavia is formed by three countries: Norway, Denmark and Sweden.

If the above statements are true, which one of the following statements must also be true?
A. Denmark is part of Scandinavia.
B. People who live in Scandinavia are called Norwegians.
C. It is always cold in Nordic countries.
D. Iceland is a Nordic country.

End of test.

| Score: | Time taken: | Target met? |

Target time: 10 minutes

■ Underline the word in brackets that is **closest** in meaning to the word in capitals.

> **Example** ERROR   (<u>mistake</u>, right, correct, answer)

1. DECEIVE   (decrease, cheat, dishevel, multiply)
2. CUNNING   (cautious, charming, sly, frustrating)
3. SINISTER   (silence, menacing, administer, welcoming)
4. VAST   (close, colossal, valley, mountain)
5. ABUNDANT   (plentiful, exacerbate, amplify, cruel)

■ Underline the two words, **one** from each group, that best complete the sentence.

> **Example** **Earth** is to (mud, dirty, <u>planet</u>) as **cow** is to (field <u>mammal</u>, bull).

6. **Monday** is to (yesterday, Tuesday, Sunday) as **Friday** is to (Wednesday, tomorrow, Thursday).
7. **Feline** is to (tiger, chicken, hound) as **canine** is to (hyena, herbivore, cheetah).
8. **Esteem** is to (favour, disregard, admire) as **continue** is to (desist, resist, coexist).
9. **Exceptional** is to (allowable, pursuable, typical) as **ignorant** is to (educated, uncultured, neglected).
10. **Scarecrow** is to (farmer, birds, field) as **mannequin** is to (shop, surgery, clothes).

■ Find the missing letters or symbols in each sequence and write them on the line. Use the alphabet to help you.

A B C D E F G H I J K L M N O P Q R S T U V W X Y Z

> **Example** Hi   Jk   Lm   No   __Pq__
> (first letter +2 capitals; second letter +2 lower case)

11. BZ   GY   QX   FW   _____
12. Az   Cx   Gt   Mn   _____
13. AA   DE   BZ   JK   CY   PQ   _____
14. R%X   S*Z   U%B   X*D   _____

■ Work out the answers. Write your answers on the lines.

15. Stefan wins the 100 metre sprint by 0.2 seconds. Finn was in second place, taking 17.75 seconds in total. How long did Stefan take? _____

16. Jon is baking biscuits for his brother's birthday party. It takes him 20 minutes' preparation time plus 12 minutes' baking time. He leaves the first batch in the oven for 15 minutes and they burn. He starts again with a new batch 5 minutes later. The biscuits are finally ready at 12.35 p.m. What time did he start making his first batch of biscuits? _____

End of test.

Score:		Time taken:		Target met?	

1–5. Look at the words in groups A, B, C and D. For each of the words below, choose the correct group and write its letter on the line.

A	B	C	D
nurse	solicitor	tutor	violinist

barrister _____   trainer _____   surgeon _____   judge _____   lecturer _____

headteacher _____   doctor _____   cellist _____   lawyer _____   flautist _____

Use the information given to answer each sum. Write your answer as a **letter**.

Example A = 10   B = 6   C = 3   D = 12   E = 18   **B × C =** _E_   (6 × 3 = 18)

6. A = 98   B = 63   C = 271   D = 350   E = 4   **B × E + A =** _____

7. A = 0.9   B = 1.1   C = 0.8   D = 4   E = 1.6   **C ÷ D + A =** _____

8. A = 123   B = 75   C = 67   D = 115   E = 95   **C + A − B =** _____

9. A = 153   B = 81   C = 17   D = 146   E = 9   **B ÷ E × C =** _____

10. A = 16   B = 33   C = 7   D = 35   E = 21   **D⁄C + A =** _____

Using the alphabet to help you, find the letter pair that completes each sentence. Write it on the line.

A B C D E F G H I J K L M N O P Q R S T U V W X Y Z

Example **FG** is to **EF** as **LM** is to _KL_.   (−1, −1)

11. **SD** is to **HW** as **GY** is to _____.   13. **DW** is to **JA** as **VF** is to _____.

12. **MO** is to **ER** as **UF** is to _____.   14. **RA** is to **TV** as **HX** is to _____.

Work out the answers. Write your answers on the lines.

15. Annie, Sarah, Rav, Jason, Sydney and Louie belong to the school gymnastics team. Annie and Rav like doing somersaults and cartwheels and they are both able to use the balance bars. Louie hasn't learned how to do somersaults or back flips but he is really good at cartwheels. Louie and Sydney can use the balance bars but Sarah can't. Sydney and Sarah both like to do somersaults and back flips but Jason only does back flips. How many people can do back flips or somersaults? _____

16. Chloe competes in the Regional Swimming Championships. She swims the **200** metre race, alongside Jennie and Andrew. Then **6** different people swim the **50** metre race and **8** more people swim the **100** metre race. Finally, Cosima swims the **20** metre butterfly race with Michael, Cameron and Alexa. How many people swim races of **25** metres or longer? _____

End of test.

Score:	Time taken:	Target met?

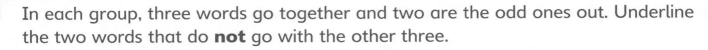

Target time: **10 minutes**

■ In each group, three words go together and two are the odd ones out. Underline the two words that do **not** go with the other three.

> **Example** <u>define</u> certain sure <u>give</u> definite

1. companion enemy foe monarch nemesis
2. pathetic damp pitiful dismal gloomy
3. danger hazard irritant risk scarce
4. grate brilliant dazzling glazed luminous
5. putrid rotten ridiculous rancid morbid

■ Underline the pair of words that are most **similar** in meaning.

> **Example** (grow, shrink) (age, young) (<u>small, little</u>)

6. (dangle, suspend) (aspect, general) (elastic, string)
7. (average, implausible) (amazement, wonder) (release, attach)
8. (caring, affectionate) (frosty, balmy) (poignant, tactile)
9. (anticipate, eager) (vile, exquisite) (lethargic, languid)
10. (mature, infantile) (bellow, under) (recalcitrant, unruly)

■ Underline the two words, **one** from each group, that best complete the sentence.

> **Example** **Earth** is to (mud, dirty, <u>planet</u>) as **cow** is to (field, <u>mammal</u>, bull).

11. **Robust** is to (fragile, tough, metallic) as **disgrace** is to (elegant, disrepute, grateful).
12. **Calm** is to (pacify, enrage, water) as **destroy** is to (disrepair, destruct, operate).
13. **Holiday** is to (pastime, leisure, family) as **workday** is to (pleasure, employ, business).
14. **Kindle** is to (book, camping, fire) as **brew** is to (potent, tea, vegetables).

■ Use the word's definition to help you fill in the missing letters.

15. T __ I __ M __ H   victory, accomplishment, achievement
16. QU __ __ Y   question, doubt, inquire

End of test.

Score:		Time taken:		Target met?	

■ Work out the missing numbers. Write them on the lines.

> **Example** 11 [88] 8   9 [54] 6   15 [___45___] 3
>
> (a × b = ?, where a represents the number on the left and b represents the number on the right)

1. 13 [76] 25   55 [160] 25   23 [_____] 19
2. 7 [4] 10   25 [20] 30   44 [_____] 28
3. 21 [80] 19   70 [152] 6   29 [_____] 2
4. 42 [61] 23   11 [8] 14   25 [_____] 49
5. 20 [80] 20   5 [20] 5   10 [_____] 10

■ Rearrange the word in capitals to make another word that goes with the first two. Write it on the line.

> **Example** jump   skip   PALE   ___LEAP___

6. circle   square   HEAPS   _____
7. kidneys   lungs   EARTH   _____
8. start   end   BEING   _____
9. kind   mean   ULCER   _____
10. noisy   loud   WORDY   _____

■ Underline **one** word from each set of brackets to complete the sentence best.

> **Example** The (<u>dentist</u>, teacher, baby) told his patient that he would have to remove the decayed (dummy, book, <u>tooth</u>).

11. I sent out (books, newspapers, invitations) asking all my friends to my birthday (cake, party, house).
12. The (surgeon, fisherman, solicitor) performed a delicate (document, operation, element) on the (patient, visitor, boat).
13. The (celebrity, daughter, criminal) arrived at the (premiere, race, prison) in a (tank, limousine, moped).
14. My (manager, vicar, neighbour) informed me that I had been (envied, promoted, promised) to a more (minor, senior, fragile) position.

■ Work out the answers. Write your answers on the lines.

15. Ben is racing his pet snails. Hotshot is in first place. Trailblazer is one place in front of Lickety, who is three places behind Whizzy. Slick is in third place, just behind Whizzy. Which snail is fourth to cross the finish line? _____

16. Eight people are taking part in a race. Bryony is coming third. Shelly is ahead of Emily and Ali but behind everybody else. Dev is two places ahead of Bryony. Damian is ahead of Simon but behind Bryony. Cindy is four places in front of Shelly. Who will cross the finish line in fourth position?

_____

End of test.

Score:		Time taken:		Target met?	

Notes for parents, tutors, teachers and other adult helpers

- **Verbal Reasoning 6** is designed for 11- and 12-year-olds, but may also be suitable for some older children.

- Remove this pull-out section before giving the book to the child.

- Before the child begins work on the first test, read together the instructions on page 2, headed **Introduction**. As you do so, look together at **Section 1 Test 1** or another of the Section 1 tests and point out to the child the different elements.

- As each question type is introduced for the first time within a particular test, an example is given. Where question types recur throughout the book, the same example is provided. This is deliberate: the example will act as a useful reminder, but children will not need to work through it repeatedly from scratch.

- Make sure that the child understands how to answer the questions and that he or she has a pencil and eraser. You should also ensure that the child is able to see a clock or a watch.

- Explain to the child how he or she should go about timing the test. Alternatively, you may wish to time the test yourself. When the child has finished the test, one of you should complete the **Time taken** box, which appears at the end of the test.

- Mark the child's work using this pull-out section, giving one mark for each correct answer (unless advised otherwise). Then complete the **Score** box at the end of the test.

- The table below shows you how to mark the **Target met?** box and the **Action** notes give you some guidance as you plan the next step. However, these are suggestions only. Please use your own judgement as you decide how best to proceed.

Score	Time taken	Target met?	Action
1–8	Any	Not yet	Give the child the previous book in the series. Provide help and support as needed.
9–13	Any	Not yet	Encourage the child to keep practising using the tests in this book. The child may need to repeat some tests. If so, wait a few weeks, or the child may simply remember the correct answers. Provide help and support as needed.
14–16	Over target – child took too long	Not yet	
14–16	On target – child took suggested time or less	Yes	Encourage the child to keep practising using further tests in this book.

- Whatever the test score, always encourage the child to have another go at the questions that he or she got wrong – without looking at the solutions. If the child's answers are still incorrect, work through these questions together. Demonstrate the correct method if necessary.

- If the child struggles with particular question types, help him or her to develop the strategies needed.

The **Understanding Reasoning** series, also available from Schofield & Sims, provides clear explanations on how to answer reasoning questions. It also provides 'Tips for tests' and 'Tips for revision'. For further details on this and other series that help children and young people to prepare for school selection tests, and for free downloads relating to the **Rapid Reasoning Tests**, visit www.schofieldandsims.co.uk

Answers

Section 1 Test 1 (page 4)

1. yield, surrender
2. adversity, misfortune
3. greedy, avaricious
4. audacity, impudence
5. eminent, famous
6. LIE (EARLIEST)
7. ERR (ERRORS)
8. OUR (JOURNEY)
9. ERA (MISERABLE)
10. END (ENDEAVOURS)
11. 1.5 (÷2 each time)
12. 520 (+75 each time)
13. 26 (add previous two numbers)
14. 49 (square numbers)
15. 13
16. 17 (including Daniel as a person from his class)

Section 1 Test 2 (page 5)

1. 9
2. 4
3. 40
4. 20
5. 20
6. gaunt, obese
7. frequent, occasional
8. estimate, calculate
9. important, trivial
10. transparent, opaque
11. 4779
12. 917
13. 2167
14. MINE
15. £1.36
16. 6

Section 1 Test 3 (page 6)

1. elated, envious (synonyms)
2. terminate, chase (synonyms)
3. comprehend, erase (synonyms)
4. illogical, specific (antonyms)
5. exact, imprecise (calculations give exact answers whereas estimations are approximate)
6. B ([56 ÷ 14] × 9 = 36)
7. C ([4200 ÷ 70] × 12 = 720)
8. A ([0.6 × 3] + 0.5 = 2.3)
9. E ([8 × 8] − 19 = 45)
10. B ([34 ÷ 17] × 21 = 42)
11. NJ (+ 4, + 4)
12. UB (−2, −2)
13. XF (−3, +1)
14. GI (−2, +2)
15. 10:31
16. 9.40 p.m./21:40

Section 1 Test 4 (page 7)

1. smart, slovenly
2. spendthrift, miser
3. wax, wane
4. superior, inferior
5. automatic, manual
6. e
7. t
8. p
9. l
10. t
11. ND (+3, −4)
12. ZE (−6, −5)
13. PF (mirror code)
14. PJ (+7, −2)
15. D
16. A

Section 1 Test 5 (page 8)

1. clef (My un<u>cle f</u>avours chocolate cake over salad!)
2. balm (The drummer's cym<u>bal m</u>akes an awfully loud noise.)
3. fond (I could not help him as I was myse<u>lf on d</u>angerous ground.)
4. lime (When I asked if you would like a gold meda<u>l I me</u>ant that you had won the race!)
5. verb (The wasp continued to ho<u>ver b</u>eside the cake.)

6. baker, break
7. beard, bared
8. being, begin
9. bores, robes
10. cruel, ulcer
11. 8 ([a + b] × 2)
12. 9 (2a − b)
13. 120 ([a + b] × 2)
14. 80 ([a + b] × 2)
15. 28 September
16. 117

Section 1 Test 6 (page 9)

1. ICE (PRICELESS)
2. BUS (ROBUST)
3. EAT or ATE (UNBEATEN)
4. DEN (RESIDENCE)
5. EVE (SEVERELY)
6. nightgown
7. newsprint
8. herring
9. bathe
10. scarlet
11. 4
12. 60
13. 1
14. 325
15. B
16. D

Section 1 Test 7 (page 10)

1. harmony
2. lethal
3. window
4. dread
5. capture
6. cymbal, cello (the others are wind instruments)
7. harpsichord, piano (the others are instruments that the player hits directly)
8. glade, oasis (the others are types of caves)
9. calm, placate (the others are synonyms for irritate)
10. renovate, refurbish (the others mean to damage the appearance of something)

11. leftover
12. invest
13. outburst
14. subdue
15. 28
16. 8

Section 1 Test 8
(page 11)

1. steal, purloin
2. malady, illness
3. encircle, surround
4. graceful, elegant
5. courteous, polite
6. RACE [RICE] [RIDE] HIDE
7. TRIP [TRAP or TRIM]
   [TRAM or PRIM] PRAM
8. BOOK [LOOK] [LOCK]
   LOCH
9. TEND [MEND] [MEAD]
   MEAL
10. SAND [HAND] [HIND]
    HINT
11. NVTJDBM (+1 from word to
    code)
12. EWTVCKPU (+2 from word
    to code)
13. ANSWER (−1 from code to
    word)
14. ICIFVSA (+4 from word to
    code)
15. 2.20 p.m./14:20
16. 150

Section 1 Test 9
(page 12)

1. postcard (all forms of
   written communication)
2. hammer (all types of tools)
3. decagon (all 2D shapes)
4. blossom (all synonyms for
   flourish)
5. saunter (all ways of walking
   in a relaxed fashion)
6. 100
7. 20
8. 2500
9. 2
10. 2.5

11. EF (+1, +1)
12. HN (0, +8)
13. FZ (first letter −1, −2 etc.;
    second letter +1, +2, etc.)
14. RX (first letter −10, −9 etc.;
    second letter +10, +9, etc.)
15. chocolate
16. 3

Section 1 Test 10
(page 13)

1. extrovert, social (the others
   refer to being alone)
2. intend, mistake (the others
   are synonyms for consider)
3. scatter, disperse (the others
   are synonyms for gather)
4. juice, rude (the others are
   synonyms for polite)
5. abbreviate, brief (the others
   are synonyms for old)
6. LIT (SOLITUDE)
7. CAN (SIGNIFICANT)
8. AND (SQUANDERED)
9. END (SURRENDERED)
10. PAR (SEPARATE)
11. IZRMUZOO (mirror code)
12. TIGER (+2 from code to
    word)
13. SCARLET (+1 from code to
    word)
14. MAXN (+1, 0, +1, 0 from
    word to code)
15. THOUGHTFUL
16. ADVANTAGE

Section 1 Test 11
(page 14)

1. idea, bleach (move l)
2. able, lances (move c)
3. paper, mother (move m)
4. bought, brawl (move r)
5. single, booth (move h)
6. C ([144 ÷ 2] ÷ 6 = 12)
7. C (−5 + 9 − 12 = −8)
8. A ([600 ÷ 50] + 108 = 120)
9. B ($\frac{1}{2} + \frac{2}{4} = 1$)
10. D ([9 × 15] ÷ 5 = 27)
11. meal

12. rope
13. male
14. loser
15. 5.35 p.m./17:35
16. 3

Section 1 Test 12
(page 15)

1. descendant
2. mobile
3. surplus
4. amiable
5. depth
6. h
7. r
8. t
9. n
10. b
11. VCZNRMZGRLM (mirror
    code)
12. MOISTURE (−1 from code to
    word)
13. VCKIVHHRLM (mirror code)
14. UKPIW (+1, +2, +3, etc.
    from word to code)
15. 31
16. 12.35 p.m.

Section 2 Test 1
(page 16)

1. 610 (+20)
2. 0.888 (÷10)
3. 256 (×2)
4. 5 (alternating +1 and ÷2)
5. 3.5 (÷2)
6. caterpillar
7. alternative
8. germinate
9. relationship
10. kitten
11. 8743
12. 78644
13. 24338
14. MOTTO
15. C
16. A

Answers

Section 2 Test 2
(page 17)

1. cheat
2. sly
3. menacing
4. colossal
5. plentiful
6. Sunday, Thursday (Sunday is the day before Monday and Thursday is the day before Friday.)
7. tiger, hyena (A tiger is a feline (cat) and a hyena is a canine (dog).)
8. disregard, desist (antonyms)
9. typical, educated (antonyms)
10. field, shop (You find a scarecrow in a field and a mannequin in a shop.)
11. 2V (+ multiples of 5, −1)
12. Uf (+ multiples of 2, − multiples of 2 and lower case letter)
13. DX (leapfrogging: +1, −1)
14. B%F (first letter +1, +2, etc.; second symbol alternating % *; third letter +2)
15. 17.55 seconds
16. 11.23 a.m.

Section 2 Test 3
(page 18)

1–5. [score half a point for each correct answer]
A: surgeon, doctor (all jobs to do with medicine)
B: barrister, judge, lawyer (all jobs to do with the law)
C: trainer, lecturer, headteacher (all jobs to do with education)
D: cellist, flautist (all musicians)
6. D ([63 × 4] + 98 = 350)
7. B ([0.8 ÷ 4] + 0.9 = 1.1)
8. D ([67 + 123] − 75 = 115)
9. A ([81 ÷ 9] × 17 = 153)
10. E ([35 ÷ 7] + 16 = 21)

11. TB (mirror code)
12. MI (−8, +3)
13. BJ (+6, +4)
14. JS (+2, −5)
15. 5 (everyone apart from Louie)
16. 17

Section 2 Test 4
(page 19)

1. companion, monarch (the others are synonyms for enemy)
2. pathetic, pitiful (the others refer to types of miserable weather)
3. irritant, scarce (the others are synonyms for danger)
4. grate, glazed (the others are synonyms for dazzling)
5. ridiculous, morbid (the others are synonyms for rotten)
6. dangle, suspend
7. amazement, wonder
8. caring, affectionate
9. lethargic, languid
10. recalcitrant, unruly
11. tough, disrepute (synonyms)
12. pacify, destruct (synonyms)
13. leisure, business (Holidays are leisure activities and workdays are business activities.)
14. fire, tea (Kindle is the precursor to fire and brew is the precursor to tea.)
15. TRIUMPH
16. QUERY

Section 2 Test 5
(page 20)

1. 84 ([a + b] × 2)
2. 60 (2a − b)
3. 62 ([a + b] × 2)
4. 1 (2a − b)
5. 40 ([a + b] × 2)
6. SHAPE
7. HEART

8. BEGIN
9. CRUEL
10. ROWDY
11. invitations, party
12. surgeon, operation, patient
13. celebrity, premiere, limousine
14. manager, promoted, senior
15. Trailblazer (order from first to last is Hotshot, Whizzy, Slick, Trailblazer, Lickety)
16. Damian (order from first to last is Dev, Cindy, Bryony, Damian, Simon, Shelly, Emily, Ali)

Section 2 Test 6
(page 21)

1. chaos
2. misery
3. disloyal
4. unknown
5. strong
6. insane
7. without
8. independent
9. message
10. director
11. E (AAEEEGGRTX)
12. I (AAEEILLTV)
13. H (ACCGHILLOOPSY)
14. L (AAAILMMMN)
15. Ruby (order from front to back of queue is Anna, Josh, Mel, Shameet, Ruby, Meg, Natalie)
16. Jana's (order of receiving food from first to last is Jeff, Gavin, Jana, Andy, Steve, Becky)

Section 2 Test 7 (page 22)

1. tact (Do not act as if you know nothing about this!)
2. wren (We know renegotiation is the only option.)
3. port (Do you want to stop or try going on?)
4. owls (The lost wolf will howl so that it can find its pack.)
5. toad (Are you going to address the letter?)
6. rush, bland (move b)
7. tier, gash (move g)
8. cape, drone (move r)
9. order, bangle (move b)
10. imply, slaughter (move s)
11. c
12. f
13. k
14. t
15. first (order from tallest to shortest is Toby, Rachel, Jeremy, Zak and Monica, Beth)
16. paint (steps: 1. attach limbs; 2. put motor in; 3. paint; 4. wire in power button)

Section 2 Test 8 (page 23)

1. PONG [GONG] [GONE] GORE
2. LAID [LAND] [HAND] HANG
3. STOOL [STOOP] [STOMP] STAMP
4. DRINK [DRANK] [CRANK] CRANE
5. TRAIN [BRAIN] [BRAID] BRAND
6. ODE (ABODE)
7. SIT (ADVERSITY)
8. AMP (AMPLE)
9. FOR (UNFORTUNATE)
10. PAT (ANTICIPATED)
11. butterfly, delicate, perched
12. pleased, cousin, visiting

13. demolished, structure, unstable
14. schoolboy, belongings, satchel
15. Tuesday
16. 2

Section 2 Test 9 (page 24)

1. tamed
2. thank
3. grape
4. bloom
5. loose
6. mile, yard (the others describe timing in music)
7. manor, story (the others describe a person)
8. willing, gruelling (the others are synonyms for stubborn)
9. erase, emit (the others are synonyms for anchor)
10. report, history (the others are synonyms for myth)
11. 2.5 (÷2)
12. 2 (alternating ÷4, +2)
13. 184 (+56)
14. 1344 (×4)
15. 11.31 a.m.
16. 8.40 a.m. in New York (1.40 p.m. UK time)

Section 2 Test 10 (page 25)

1. tyre (The party remained noisy and crowded until midnight.)
2. gaze (Chasing a zebra makes good hunting practice for young lion cubs.)
3. exit (If you can read the index it's bound to be there.)
4. echo (She chose the pink coat to complement her green dress.)
5. sore (Birds may eat worms or even slugs.)
6. stagecoach
7. airway

8. carrot
9. lifeline
10. thankless
11. clock (What time does the plane depart to Paris?)
12. they (My family and I live in a bungalow.)
13. his (She was delighted to pass all her exams.)
14. the (What is your favourite time of the year?)
15. 10/50 or 1/5 of the time (10 mins out of 50 mins)
16. 15 km/hour (There are 4 lots of 250 m in 1 km so it would take 4 minutes to travel 1 km and therefore 15 km in 1 hour.)

Section 2 Test 11 (page 26)

1. sender, planting (move l)
2. prove, pedal (move d)
3. light, flame (move f)
4. haven, ships (move s)
5. insect, pounce (move p)
6. 10
7. 100
8. 9
9. 7.5
10. 1.5
11. OkR (first letter +1; second letter −1 and lower case; third letter +1)
12. Vk (leapfrogging: first letter +1; second letter −1 lower case)
13. mM (first letter alternating i and m; second letter +1 each time)
14. YT (first letter −2; second letter +3)
15. 13 November (If 25 October is a Monday, 1 and 8 November are also Mondays; therefore the Saturday after Monday 8 will be 13 November.)
16. 4 Fridays (on 5, 12, 19, 26 August)

Answers

Section 2 Test 12
(page 27)

1. speech
2. bitter
3. bear
4. fire
5. mole
6. air, helicopter (*Helicopters* are a form of *air* transport.)
7. Olympic, ambition (My *ambition* is to be an *Olympic* gymnast.)
8. will, weather (Whatever the *weather*, the match *will* go ahead.)
9. leap, are (There *are* three hundred and sixty-six days in a *leap* year.)
10. of, capital (Paris is the *capital* city *of* France.)
11. haven
12. reserved
13. distant
14. bigoted
15. £8.55 more
16. 9.38 a.m.

Section 3 Test 1
(page 28)

1–5. *[score half a point for each correct answer]*
A: stubborn, wilful, inflexible (synonyms for obstinate)
B: retract, withdraw (synonyms for revoke)
C: timely, prompt (synonyms for punctual)
D: famous, well-known, important (synonyms for prominent)
6. wave (I sa<u>w a v</u>entriloquist at the theatre.)
7. soul (This route is shorter <u>so ul</u>timately we will get there sooner.)
8. nine (The carousel spu<u>n in</u> endless circles.)
9. slit (I gues<u>s lit</u>tle dogs are

welcome in the hotel.)
10. dent (The o<u>ld ent</u>ertainers are usually the funniest.)
11. SOUL
12. GVOVKSLMV (mirror code)
13. WVORXRLFH (mirror code)
14. GREAT (position of letters in the alphabet where A=1, B=2, C=3, etc.)
15. ABSCOND
16. MANUSCRIPT

Section 3 Test 2
(page 29)

1. 12 ([a − b] × 2)
2. 28 (2a + b)
3. 75 (a ÷ [b ÷ 2])
4. 32 (a × 2b) or 2(a × b)
5. 29 (7a + b)
6. PETROL
7. MIRROR
8. COFFEE
9. WARMED
10. STORM
11. PAR (APPARITION)
12. TON (ASTONISHED)
13. CAT (CATASTROPHIC)
14. MEN (COMMENCE)
15. 8.55 a.m. (It takes him 20 minutes to travel 7 miles at 21 miles per hour.)
16. 2.5 km per hour

Section 3 Test 3
(page 30)

1. anything, like (Goats *like* to eat *anything* they can find!)
2. enormous, fisherman (The *fisherman* caught an *enormous* eel.)
3. afternoon, strawberries (I like *strawberries* and cream for *afternoon* tea!)
4. for, congratulated (The teacher *congratulated* her class *for* their hard work.)
5. millions, roamed (Dinosaurs *roamed* the Earth *millions* of years ago.)

6. box
7. table
8. date
9. watch
10. crane
11. 3692
12. 8423
13. 986462
14. GNAW
15. Alex (order of arrival is Alex, Becki, Leo and Kate together, then Kara)
16. Poppy (order from left to right is Anne, James, Rishi, Max, Fran, Poppy)

Section 3 Test 4
(page 31)

1. mechanic (mechanism, mechanic, manoeuvre, machine, machinate)
2. voluminous (volunteer, voluminous, volume, vocation, vacation)
3. knitted (knotted, knitted, kneaded, kinetic, kinaesthetic)
4. course (court, course, courgette, count, colour)
5. obstruction (obtuse, obstruction, obstacle, oblong, obese)
6. KY (−3, −5)
7. ML (+8, −2)
8. EI (mirror code)
9. LS (+ 4, −5)
10. YX (−3, −2)
11. par (partake, parable, pardon, parrot)
12. ten (tenant, tendon, tenfold, tenable)
13. con (concourse, contact, content, condescend)
14. ram (rampant, rampage, ramrod, ramshackle)
15. £13.80
16. 2/12 or 1/6

Section 3 Test 5 (page 32)

1. leek, soften (move s)
2. fume, drivel (move l)
3. moor, trust (move t)
4. arch, manger (move m)
5. left, chide (move c)
6. C ([750 + 250] – 550 = 450)
7. B ([549 ÷ 9] + 9 = 70)
8. B ([2 × 19] ÷ [14 ÷ 7] = 19)
9. B ([–10 – 4] + 17 = 3)
10. D ([310 – 34] ÷ 2 = 138)
11. SI (+5, –5)
12. YQ (first letter +8,+ 4,+2,+1; second letter +1,+2,+ 4,+8)
13. XC (first letter alternating +10, +5; second letter alternating +10, +5)
14. WR (W and X alternate, +1)
15. Lulu and Macey (order of the pairs from front to back is Lulu and Macey, Stella and Tim, Jack and Zhu, Melissa and Lewis, then Sam and Georgie)
16. Fred (order from front to back of the rope is Carys, Sara, Heather, Christopher, Fred, Angus, Marcus, Johnny)

Section 3 Test 6 (page 33)

1. B ([24 ÷ 2] × 12 = 144)
2. D ([100 – 65] ÷ 5 = 7)
3. A (7 × 14 × 0 = 0)
4. E ([25 – 45] + 36 = 16)
5. C ([55 ÷ 5] × 3 = 33)
6. TEAR
7. €∞©i
8. ↑□□◊
9. RATS
10. VIEW (position of each letter in the alphabet plus 10: A=11, B=12, C=13, etc.)
11. instigate, initiate
12. sprightly, nimble
13. annual, yearly
14. mainstream, conventional
15. SURREAL
16. VINDICTIVE

Section 3 Test 7 (page 34)

1. pig (pigtail, pigpen, pigeon, piglet)
2. sun (sundry, sunbathe, sunshine, sunburn)
3. pan (pantry, pancake, panpipes, panache)
4. hand (handsome, handcuff, handbook, handmade)
5. horse (horseplay, horsehair, horsefly, horseradish)
6. a
7. d
8. g
9. n
10. m
11. word (We will no**w ord**er dessert, please.)
12. reed (Take a spa**re ed**ition of the textbook from the professor's office.)
13. mast (My friend wants to ski**m a st**one across the lake.)
14. peak (Is a large a**pe a k**ind of monkey?)
15. 172 800 (60 secs × 60 mins × 48 hours)
16. 4 hours 14 mins 55 secs

Section 3 Test 8 (page 35)

1. 50 (a + b)
2. 53 (a + 2b)
3. 10 (4a – b)
4. 36 (5a + b)
5. 33 (3a + b)
6. immense, minute
7. liberty, captivity
8. help, hindrance
9. tranquil, agitated
10. obstinate, flexible
11. SLIP [SLAP or FLIP] [FLAP] FLAN
12. MILK [SILK] [SILT] SALT
13. GRAIN [BRAIN] [BRAWN] BRAWL
14. SLICE [SLIDE] [GLIDE] GLADE
15. C
16. B

Section 3 Test 9 (page 36)

1. misery (alltypes of emotions)
2. canyon (all land features that cut into the land)
3. toucan (all types of bird)
4. meteorite (all found in space)
5. thesaurus (all types of reference book)
6. upwards, sideways (synonyms)
7. valuable, inexpensive (Gold is worth a lot of money but tin is not.)
8. avoid, disgusting (synonyms)
9. fictitious, dissuade (antonyms)
10. infamous, uncover (synonyms)
11. lose
12. row
13. knit
14. beds
15. 25
16. 4.25 p.m./16:25

Answers

Section 3 Test 10 (page 37)

1. A ([10 × 10] + [2 × 2 × 2] = 108)
2. C (10 × 6 × 60 = 3600)
3. B ([27 × 2] ÷ 6 = 9)
4. D ($\frac{2}{4} - \frac{1}{2} = 0$)
5. A ([99 ÷ 3] + 17 = 50)
6. jumper, shirt (the others are types of material)
7. harmony, tranquillity (the others are synonyms for uproar)
8. exit, upstairs (the others are synonyms for captivate: note that 'entrance' has two possible meanings)
9. earth, ground (the others are all elements)
10. reckless, spiteful (the others are synonyms for kind)
11. ZJ (+7, +4)
12. CA (−6, +3)
13. SE (mirror code)
14. FG (+2, −6)
15. 38%
16. 44

Section 3 Test 11 (page 38)

1. understandable, operational (antonyms)
2. book, bookcase (Pages form a book and shelves form a bookcase.)
3. claim, abandon (synonyms)
4. standard, rotten (synonyms)
5. century, decade (There are 100 years in a century and 10 years in a decade.)
6. 34 (−9)
7. 64 (×2)
8. 9 (alternating)
9. 59 (alternating −1, +2)
10. 87 (+20)
11. t
12. o
13. y
14. l
15. 400 pages
16. 24

Section 3 Test 12 (page 39)

1. 50
2. 10
3. 10
4. 450
5. 30
6. accidental, intentional
7. summon, dismiss
8. luxury, squalor
9. fantasy, reality
10. incompetent, capable
11. 2996
12. 74969
13. 217796
14. SEEDS
15. C
16. B

This book of answers is a pull-out section from
Rapid Reasoning Tests: Verbal Reasoning 6

Published by Schofield & Sims Ltd,
Dogley Mill, Fenay Bridge, Huddersfield HD8 0NQ, UK
Telephone 01484 607080
www.schofieldandsims.co.uk

Copyright © Schofield & Sims Ltd, 2014

Author: **Siân Goodspeed**. Siân Goodspeed has asserted her moral right under the Copyright, Designs and Patents Act, 1988, to be identified as the author of this work.

British Library Cataloguing in Publication Data. A catalogue record for this book is available from the British Library.

Commissioned by **Carolyn Richardson Publishing Services** (www.publiserve.co.uk)

Design by **Oxford Designers & Illustrators**
Printed in India by **Multivista Global Ltd**

ISBN 978 07217 1243 7

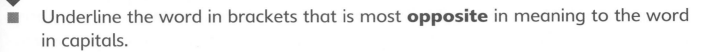

Target time: **10 minutes**

■ Underline the word in brackets that is most **opposite** in meaning to the word in capitals.

Example LOUD   (noisy, <u>quiet</u>, shout, roar)

1. ORDER   (task, direct, chaos, assign)
2. JOY   (confusion, misery, jealousy, peace)
3. FAITHFUL   (disloyal, hopeful, reliable, honest)
4. RENOWNED   (forgiven, unknown, forlorn, famous)
5. WRETCHED   (sympathetic, stealthy, strong, weak)

■ Underline the **two** words, one from each group, that together make one new word. The word from the first group comes first.

Example (<u>tea</u>, coffee, cream)   (drink, <u>room</u>, milk)   (tearoom)

6. (in, around, outside)   (sane, safe, help)
7. (with, partner, friend)   (out, inn, room)
8. (inn, in, one)   (reliable, good, dependent)
9. (mess, state, tidy)   (old, age, young)
10. (straight, blunt, direct)   (either, or, any)

■ If the letters in the word were listed in alphabetical order, which letter would come **fifth**? Write the answer on the line.

Example DANCING   <u>I</u>   (ACDGINN)

11. EXAGGERATE   ____
12. ALLEVIATE   ____
13. PSYCHOLOGICAL   ____
14. MAMMALIAN   ____

■ Work out the answers. Write your answers on the lines.

15. Seven people are waiting for a bus. Ruby is three places behind Josh, who is standing in front of Mel. Anna is two places ahead of Mel. Natalie is two places behind Ruby who is in front of Meg. Shameet is standing in front of Ruby, right in the middle of the queue. Who will be the fifth person to get on the bus when it arrives? _____

16. Becky has gone to a restaurant with five friends and they are waiting for their food to be served. Becky's meal is last to arrive. Gavin's meal arrives before Jana's but after Jeff's. Jana's meal is served before Andy's. Steve's food arrives after Andy's. Whose meal is third to arrive? _____

End of test.

Score:		Time taken:		Target met?	

■ Find the **four-letter word** hidden across two or more consecutive words in each sentence below. The order of the letters must stay the same. Underline the word and write it on the line.

Example I like lots <u>of tr</u>eacle on my porridge!   <u>soft</u>

1. Do not act as if you know nothing about this! _____

2. We know renegotiation is the only option. _____

3. Do you want to stop or try going on? _____

4. The lost wolf will howl so that it can find its pack. _____

5. Are you going to address the letter? _____

■ Move one letter from the first word to the second word to make two new words. Write the two new words on the lines.

Example trip, star   <u>rip</u> , <u>start</u>   (move the t)

6. brush, land   _____, _____

7. tiger, ash   _____, _____

8. caper, done   _____, _____

9. border, angle   _____, _____

10. simply, laughter   _____, _____

■ Find **one** missing letter that completes **both** pairs of words. Write it on the lines.

Example strea [m] ile   doo [m] arry

11. tragi [__] omet   garli [__] ounter

12. aloo [__] lare   ree [__] ree

13. stor [__] ilo   dus [__] iln

14. clou [__] rawl   debu [__] high

■ Work out the answers. Write your answers on the lines.

15. Six people line up in height order from tallest to shortest. Jeremy is third from the front of the line. Beth is three places behind him. Rachel is not the tallest but she is taller than Zak and Monica. In what place in the line is Toby standing? _____

16. Gita is following instructions to make a robot. There are four steps to follow. She is not supposed to paint the robot or put the motor in until after she has attached the arms and legs but, if she paints the robot before the motor is in, the robot will not work. The last thing to do is to wire in the power button. What is the third thing that Gita does to make the robot? _____

End of test.

Score:		Time taken:		Target met?	

■ Change the first word into the last word. Only change **one** letter at a time, making two new words in the middle.

Example GILT [__SILT__][__SALT__] MALT

1. PONG [_____][_____] GORE
2. LAID [_____][_____] HANG
3. STOOL [_____][_____] STAMP

4. DRINK [_____][_____] CRANE
5. TRAIN [_____][_____] BRAND

■ In each of the sentences below, the word in capitals has three letters missing. Those three letters spell a word. Write the three-letter word on the line.

Example He was much **TER** than his younger brother. ___ALL___ (TALLER)

6. My **AB** was warm and homely. _____
7. She had overcome **ADVERY** to become successful. _____
8. His friend lent him **LE** money to buy a car. _____
9. The accident was **UNTUNATE**. _____
10. He **ANTICIED** that the weather would be fine for the picnic. _____

■ Underline **one** word from each set of brackets to complete the sentence best.

Example The (dentist, teacher, baby) told his patient that he would have to remove the decayed (dummy, book, tooth).

11. The (banjo, scorpion, butterfly) fluttered its (monochrome, delicate, repellent) wings as it (perched, stumbled, leant) upon a flower.

12. She was (pleased, distressed, annoyed) to hear that her favourite (canine, cousin, barrister) would be (evicting, trespassing, visiting) soon.

13. The building was (elevated, demolished, demonstrated) because its (paint, wallpaper, structure) was (unstable, forgotten, undamaged).

14. The (convict, schoolboy, fireman) carried his (cutlery, companion, belongings) in his (helmet, satchel, desktop).

■ Work out the answers. Write your answers on the lines.

15. If 8 February is a Friday, what day will 5 March be in a non-leap year? _____

16. How many fewer days are there altogether in November and September than in January and March? _____

End of test.

Score:		Time taken:		Target met?	

Target time: **10 minutes**

The word in square brackets has been made by some of the letters from the two outside words. Make a new word in the middle of the second group of words in the same way. Write the new word on the line.

Example (help [hear] pair)   (soup [__sort__] grit)

1. (later [learn] earned)   (three [_____] amidst)
2. (wizen [prize] proud)   (tanks [_____] think)
3. (spray [spare] reaps)   (grind [_____] pears)
4. (thirst [shirt] rushed)   (gloom [_____] sable)
5. (swing [twins] newts)   (goose [_____] stole)

In each group, three words go together and two are the odd ones out. Underline the **two** words that do **not** go with the other three.

Example <u>define</u>   certain   sure   <u>give</u>   definite

6. mile   tempo   beat   rhythm   yard
7. manner   demeanour   character   manor   story
8. willing   stubborn   inflexible   obstinate   gruelling
9. anchor   erase   cement   entrench   emit
10. report   myth   fable   history   legend

Find the missing number in each sequence and write it on the line.

Example 7   14   __21__   28   35   42   (+7 each time)

11. 80   40   20   10   5   _____   13. 16   72   128   _____   240
12. 88   22   24   6   8   _____   14. 21   84   336   _____   5376

Work out the answers. Write your answers on the lines.

15. Rinnie and Varma are meeting in the shopping mall at 11.30 a.m. Rinnie's watch is 10 minutes fast and when she arrives it shows the time as 11.35 a.m. Varma arrives 6 minutes after Rinnie. What is the real time when Varma arrives? _____

16. London is 5 hours ahead of New York. Stella leaves London at 6.35 a.m. UK time. The flight is usually 6 hours 45 minutes long but it is slowed down by turbulence and takes 20 minutes longer than usual. What will the time be in New York when Stella arrives? _____   End of test.

Score:		Time taken:		Target met?	

Target time: 10 minutes

Find the **four-letter word** hidden across two or more consecutive words in each sentence below. The order of the letters must stay the same. Underline the word and write it on the line.

Example I like lots <u>of tre</u>acle on my porridge!   <u>soft</u>

1. The party remained noisy and crowded until midnight. _____

2. Chasing a zebra makes good hunting practice for young lion cubs. _____

3. If you can read the index it's bound to be in there. _____

4. She chose the pink coat to complement her green dress. _____

5. Birds may eat worms or even slugs. _____

Underline the **two** words, one from each group, that together make one new word. The word from the first group comes first.

Example (<u>tea</u>, coffee, cream)   (drink, <u>room</u>, milk)   (tearoom)

6. (theatre, stage, act)   (carriage, coach, teach)

7. (air, oxygen, breath)   (mask, plain, way)

8. (car, journey, vehicle)   (mould, rot, die)

9. (drop, life, jump)   (stick, line, straight)

10. (talk, thank, wist)   (less, you, full)

The words in the sentences below have been muddled up and an extra, unnecessary word has been added to each. Unjumble the sentences, then remove the extra word so that the sentences make sense. Cross out the extra word.

Example how you sandwiches would ~~much~~ many like   (How many sandwiches would you like?)

11. does time the clock plane what depart to Paris

12. bungalow and I live family in a they my

13. exams she was to pass delighted all her his

14. is what time the favourite of the year your

Work out the answers. Write your answers on the lines.

15. Terry takes **35** minutes to complete his maths exam paper. He then spends **5** minutes checking his answers and the rest of the time gazing out the window. If the exam was meant to take **50** minutes, what proportion of that time did Terry spend gazing out the window? _____

16. Mrs Moggins' hat blew away in a sudden gust of wind. It travelled for **250** metres before alighting on a tree **1** minute later. How fast was it travelling in km/hr? _____

End of test.

Score:	Time taken:	Target met?

Section 2 Test 11

Move one letter from the first word to the second word to make two new words. Write the two new words on the lines.

> **Example** trip, star _____rip_____, _____start_____ (move the t)

1. slender, panting _____, _____
2. proved, peal _____, _____
3. flight, lame _____, _____
4. shaven, hips _____, _____
5. inspect, ounce _____, _____

Find the missing number in each of these equations and write it on the line.

> **Example** $20 - 5 = 12 +$ ___3___

6. $660 ÷ 6 = 11 ×$ _____
7. $110 × 120 = 132 ×$ _____
8. $48 - 59 = -20 +$ _____
9. $325 ÷ 2 = 170 -$ _____
10. $6 (2.5 + 7.75) = 60 +$ _____

Find the missing letters in each sequence and write them on the line. Use the alphabet to help you.

A B C D E F G H I J K L M N O P Q R S T U V W X Y Z

> **Example** Hi   Jk   Lm   No   __Pq__
> (first letter +2 capitals; second letter +2 lower case)

11. LnO   MmP   NlQ   _____   PjS   QiT
12. Sn   Xy   Tm   Za   Ul   Bc   _____
13. iJ   mK   iL   _____   iN   mO
14. AQ   _____   WW   UZ   SC   QF

Work out the answers. Write your answers on the lines.

15. Jackson is organising a party for his mother's 70th birthday on 8 November. He is planning the party for the Saturday after her birthday. If it is Monday 25 October now, what will be the date of his mother's party? _____

16. How many Fridays will there be in August if 9 July is a Saturday? _____

End of test.

Score:		Time taken:		Target met?	

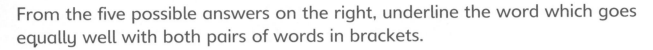

Target time: 10 minutes

■ From the five possible answers on the right, underline the word which goes equally well with both pairs of words in brackets.

Example (expensive, pricey)   (cherished, valued)   cheap   <u>dear</u>   precious   costly   loved

1. (talk, presentation)   (language, words)   voice   letter   speech   performance   audience
2. (freezing, chilly)   (sour, acidic)   winter   cold   ice   bitter   tart
3. (carry, support)   (tolerate, endure)   lift   accept   bear   withstand   hold
4. (shoot, discharge)   (flame, blaze)   fire   aim   explode   burn   gun
5. (spy, infiltrator)   (vole, rat)   agent   mole   detective   mouse   observe

■ Underline the **two** words in each sentence that need to change places in order for the sentence to make sense.

Example How do <u>your</u> like <u>you</u> tea?   (How do <u>you</u> like <u>your</u> tea?)

6. air are a form of helicopters transport
7. my Olympic is to be an ambition gymnast
8. whatever the will, the match weather go ahead
9. there leap three hundred and sixty-six days in a are year
10. Paris is the of city capital France

■ Underline the word in brackets that is **closest** in meaning to the word in capitals.

Example ERROR   (<u>mistake</u>, right, correct, answer)

11. SANCTUARY   (secret, haven, aquarium, desert)
12. RETICENT   (reserved, enthused, empowered, volatile)
13. REMOTE   (receive, likely, control, distant)
14. PREJUDICED   (just, bigoted, wise, proud)

■ Work out the answers. Write your answers on the lines.

15. Matthew earns £5.70 an hour on his paper round. His paper round normally takes him 2 hours, but today he has extra papers to deliver and it has taken him $3\frac{1}{2}$ hours. How much more has Matthew earned from today's paper round? _____

16. Mona arrived at the doctor's surgery at 9 a.m. She spoke to the receptionist for 4 minutes and then waited in the waiting room for 14 minutes. Her appointment lasted 13 minutes and then she walked home taking 7 minutes. What time did she get home? _____

End of test.

Score:	Time taken:	Target met?

Section 3 Test 1

↓

■ 1–5. Look at the words in groups A, B, C and D. For each of the words below, choose the correct group and write its letter on the line.

A	B	C	D
obstinate	revoke	punctual	prominent

timely _____   stubborn _____   famous _____   retract _____   well-known _____

prompt _____   withdraw _____   wilful _____   inflexible _____   important _____

■ Find the **four-letter word** hidden across two or more consecutive words in each sentence below. The order of the letters must stay the same. Underline the word and write it on the line.

> **Example** I like lots of treacle on my porridge!   ___soft___

6. I saw a ventriloquist at the theatre. _____

7. This route is shorter so ultimately we will get there sooner. _____

8. The carousel spun in endless circles. _____

9. I guess little dogs are welcome in the hotel. _____

10. The old entertainers are usually the funniest. _____

■ Using the alphabet to help you, crack the code. Write the answer on the line.

A B C D E F G H I J K L M N O P Q R S T U V W X Y Z

> **Example** If the code for **SIT** is **TJU**, what is the code for **SAT**? ___TBU___
>
> (+1 from the word to the code)

11. If the code for **LOUSE** is **$!*+5**, what does the code **+!*$** mean? _____

12. If the code for **TOOTHACHE** is **GLLGSZXSV**, what is **TELEPHONE** in code? _____

13. If the code for **CHOCOLATE** is **XSLXLOZGV**, what is **DELICIOUS** in code? _____

14. If the code **4, 5, 1, 18** means **DEAR**, what does the code **7, 18, 5, 1, 20** mean? _____

■ Use the word's definition to help you fill in the missing letters.

15. AB __ __ O __ D   escape, flee, desert

16. MA __ __ S __ RI __ T   music, document, text

End of test.

Score:		Time taken:		Target met?	

Target time: **10 minutes**

■ Work out the missing numbers. Write them on the lines.

Example 11 [88] 8   9 [54] 6   15 [___45___] 3
(a × b = ?, where a represents the number on the left and b represents the number on the right)

1. 44 [64] 12   56 [100] 6   24 [_____] 18
2. 28 [60] 4   10 [25] 5   12 [_____] 4
3. 86 [43] 4   24 [12] 4   150 [_____] 4

4. 9 [54] 3   4 [48] 6   8 [_____] 2
5. 2 [15] 1   3 [23] 2   4 [_____] 1

■ Rearrange the letters in capitals to make a new word so that the sentence makes sense. Write the new word on the line.

Example It was a dark and windy **GTHIN**.   ___NIGHT___

6. The car ground to a halt because it had no **LOTPRE**.   _____
7. The clown checked his makeup in the **RMRIRO**.   _____
8. **FCFEEO** was the only thing that woke Mary up in the morning.   _____
9. After a long rainy walk the dogs **DMRAEW** themselves by the fire.   _____
10. The **MTSRO** rolled in over the hills making everything gloomy.   _____

■ In each of the sentences below, the word in capitals has three letters missing. Those three letters spell a word. Write the three-letter word on the line.

Example He was much **TER** than his younger brother.   ___ALL___   (TALLER)

11. The ghostly **APITION** scared me.   _____
12. The boy was **ASISHED** that he had won the prize.   _____
13. The earthquake caused **ASTROPHIC** damage.   _____
14. He waited for the lesson to **COMCE**.   _____

■ Work out the answers. Write your answers on the lines.

15. Jaden travels to work on his bicycle at an average speed of **21** miles per hour. He needs to arrive in work at **9.15** a.m. in order to change and get ready for his start time of **9.30** a.m. If he lives **7** miles away from work, what time does he need to set out?   _____

16. Izabell takes part in a sponsored walk. She takes 4 hours to walk the full distance of 10 km. What is her average speed?   _____

End of test.

Score:	Time taken:	Target met?

⬇ ■ Underline the **two** words in each sentence that need to change places in order for the sentence to make sense.

Example How do <u>your</u> like <u>you</u> tea? (How do <u>you</u> like <u>your</u> tea?)

1. goats anything to eat like they can find
2. the enormous caught an fisherman eel
3. I like afternoon and cream for strawberries tea
4. the teacher for her class congratulated their hard work
5. dinosaurs millions the Earth roamed of years ago

■ From the five possible answers on the right, underline the word which goes equally well with both pairs of words in brackets.

Example (expensive, pricey) (cherished, valued) cheap <u>dear</u> precious costly loved

6. (fight, punch) (container, cuboid)   hit box beat vessel cube
7. (counter, desk) (chart, graph)   plot worktop diagram data table
8. (day, month) (meeting, appointment)   year engagement date calendar conference
9. (clock, timepiece) (observe, see)   watch notice stopwatch witness timer
10. (hoist, winch) (stork, flamingo)   lift pelican crane pulley crank

■ Match the number codes to the words. One code is missing. Use this to help you work out the answers to the questions. Write your answers on the lines.

SWING   GANG   AGAIN   SWAN   38462   92946   2962

What is the code for:

11. **SNAG**? _____   12. **WIGS**? _____   13. **AWNING**? _____
14. What does the code **2698** mean? _____

■ Work out the answers. Write your answers on the lines.

15. Becki and her friends are meeting up at a cafe. Alex arrives first and Kara arrives last. Leo and Kate arrive at the same time, just before Kara. Who does Becki arrive after? _____

16. A class of students is posing for a school photograph. In the top row, are six students. Anne is on the far left, next to James. Between James and Poppy, there is Rishi, Max and Fran. Who is on the far right? _____

End of test.

Score:		Time taken:		Target met?	

Target time: 10 minutes

If these words were listed in **reverse alphabetical order**, which word would come **second**? Write the answer on the line.

> **Example** improve   impress   empower   emperor   ample   _impress_

1. mechanic   machine   mechanism   machinate   manoeuvre   _____
2. volume   volunteer   vocation   vacation   voluminous   _____
3. kinetic   knotted   knitted   kneaded   kinaesthetic   _____
4. colour   count   course   courgette   court   _____
5. obstacle   oblong   obese   obtuse   obstruction   _____

Using the alphabet to help you, find the letter pair that completes each sentence. Write it on the line.

A B C D E F G H I J K L M N O P Q R S T U V W X Y Z

> **Example** **FG** is to **EF** as **LM** is to _KL_.   (–1, –1)

6. **BG** is to **YB** as **ND** is to _____.
7. **OT** is to **WR** as **EN** is to _____.
8. **XO** is to **CL** as **VR** is to _____.
9. **WD** is to **AY** as **HX** is to _____.
10. **PN** is to **ML** as **BZ** is to _____.

Each word below can be changed into a new word by putting another word in **front** of it. The added word should be the **same** for each word in the row. Find the added word and write it on the line.

> **Example** buoy   line   boat   style   _life_

11. take   able   don   rot   _____
12. ant   don   fold   able   _____
13. course   tact   tent   descend   _____
14. pant   page   rod   shackle   _____

Work out the answers. Write your answers on the lines.

15. Marit has a budget of £20 for her charity bake sale. A pack of flour costs £2.20 and a packet of butter is £1.50. Marit also needs a pint of milk, at £1, and a pack of sugar. Two packs of sugar costs £3.00. How much change will Marit have once she has bought all her ingredients? _____

16. Kim is choosing a kitten. There are 12 kittens in the litter, 4 of which are white. Half the litter are black and the rest are grey. What is the probability that Kim chooses a grey kitten? _____

End of test.

Score:		Time taken:		Target met?	

Move one letter from the first word to the second word to make two new words. Write the two new words on the lines.

| **Example** trip, star | ____rip____ , ____start____ | (move the t) |

1. sleek, often _____ , _____
2. flume, drive _____ , _____
3. motor, rust _____ , _____
4. march, anger _____ , _____
5. cleft, hide _____ , _____

Use the information given to answer each sum. Write your answer as a **letter**.

| **Example** A = 10   B = 6   C = 3   D = 12   E = 18   **B × C =** __E__   (6 × 3 = 18) |

6. A = 550   B = 250   C = 450   D = 350   E = 750   **E + B – A =** _____
7. A = 9   B = 70   C = 549   D = 68   E = 79   **C ÷ A + A =** _____
8. A = 7   B = 19   C = 11   D = 14   E = 127   **2B ÷ (D ÷ A) =** _____
9. A = 17   B = 3   C = –10   D = –1   E = 4   **(C – E) + A =** _____
10. A = 155   B = 34   C = 310   D = 138   E = 2   **(C – B) ÷ E =** _____

Find the missing letters in each sequence and write them on the line. Use the alphabet to help you.

A B C D E F G H I J K L M N O P Q R S T U V W X Y Z

| **Example** Hi   Jk   Lm   No   __Pq__ |
| (first letter +2 capitals; second letter +2 lower case) |

11. YC   DX   IS   NN   _____
12. JB   RC   VE   XI   _____
13. TY   DI   IN   SX   _____
14. WP   XQ   _____   XS   WT

Work out the answers. Write your answers on the lines.

15. Ten children are holding hands in a crocodile line. Sam and Georgie are at the back. Stella and Tim are in front of Jack and Zhu but behind Lulu and Macey. Melissa and Lewis are fourth in the line. Which pair are at the front? _____ and _____

16. Carys is part of her school tug-of-war team. She is at the front of the rope and Sara is behind her. Johnny is at the back with Marcus in front of him. Angus is in front of Marcus and Fred is in front of him. Christopher and Heather are between Fred and Sara, with the three girls behind one another. Who is fifth on the rope? _____

End of test.

| Score: | | Time taken: | | Target met? | |

Target time: 10 minutes

■ Use the information given to answer each sum. Write your answer as a **letter**.

Example A = 10   B = 6   C = 3   D = 12   E = 18   **B × C =** ___E___   (6 × 3 = 18)

1. A = 24   B = 144   C = 12   D = 132   E = 2   **C × A ÷ E =** _____
2. A = 5   B = 100   C = 65   D = 7   E = 77   **(B – C) ÷ A =** _____
3. A = 0   B = 14   C = 98   D = 7   E = 64   **D × B × A =** _____
4. A = 36   B = 45   C = 25   D = 27   E = 16   **(C – B) + A =** _____
5. A = 55   B = 5   C = 33   D = 21   E = 3   **E × A ÷ B =** _____

■ Using the alphabet to help you, crack the code. Write the answer on the line.

A B C D E F G H I J K L M N O P Q R S T U V W X Y Z

Example If the code for **SIT** is **TJU**, what is the code for **SAT**?   ___TBU___

(+ 1 from the word to the code)

6. If the code **^&"£^** means **TREAT**, what does the code **^"£&** mean? _____
7. If **DAZZLE** is written in code as **€∞©©¤¡**, what is the code for **DAZE**? _____
8. If the code for **ROOMY** is **◊□□↑Δ**, what is the code for **MOOR**? _____
9. If the code for **STAR** is **∫∑∏∂**, what does the code **∂∏∑∫** mean? _____
10. If **DRIVE** is written in code as **14, 28, 19, 32, 15**, what does the code **32, 19, 15, 33** mean? _____

■ Underline the pair of words that are most **similar** in meaning.

Example (grow, shrink)   (age, young)   (small, little)

11. (instigate, initiate)   (hope, pathos)   (allay, friend)
12. (enthuse, dampen)   (sprightly, nimble)   (resolute, courteous)
13. (annual, yearly)   (advent, calendar)   (egotistical, brave)
14. (excuse, blame)   (baron, peasant)   (mainstream, conventional)

■ Use the word's definition to help you fill in the missing letters.

15. SU __ __ E __ L   bizarre, strange, dreamlike
16. VI __ __ IC __ IV __   malicious, spiteful, mean

End of test.

| Score: | | Time taken: | | Target met? | |

■ Each word below can be changed into a new word by putting another word in **front**. The added word should be the **same** for each word in the row. Find the added word and write it on the line.

Example buoy line boat style ___*life*___

1. tail pen eon let _____
2. dry bathe shine burn _____
3. try cake pipes ache _____

4. some cuff book made _____
5. play hair fly radish _____

■ Find **one** missing letter that completes **both** pairs of words. Write it on the lines.

Example strea [_m_] ile   doo [_m_] arry

6. cobr [___] brupt   quot [___] ward
7. shoul [___] rake   flui [___] rift
8. sprun [___] awk   strin [___] ale
9. shor [___] ape   spaw [___] otch
10. ato [___] irth   chas [___] arry

■ Find the **four-letter word** hidden across two or more consecutive words in each sentence below. The order of the letters must stay the same. Underline the word and write it on the line.

Example I like lots <u>of trea</u>cle on my porridge! ___*soft*___

11. We will now order dessert, please. _____
12. Take a spare edition of the textbook from the professor's office. _____
13. My friend wants to skim a stone across the lake. _____
14. Is a large ape a kind of monkey? _____

■ Work out the answers. Write your answers on the lines.

15. How many seconds are there in 2 days? _____
16. Miles beats his friend, Troy, in a marathon by 10 minutes 15 seconds. If Troy took 4 hours 25 minutes 10 seconds, how long did Miles take? _____

End of test.

Score:		Time taken:		Target met?	

Target time: 10 minutes

■ Work out the missing numbers. Write them on the lines.

Example 11 [88] 8   9 [54] 6   15 [__45__] 3
(a × b = ?, where a represents the number on the left and b represents the number on the right)

1. 17 [20] 3   42 [50] 8   36 [_____] 14   4. 2 [17] 7   4 [23] 3   7 [_____] 1
2. 5 [35] 15   2 [98] 48   5 [_____] 24   5. 3 [10] 1   4 [15] 3   10 [_____] 3
3. 2 [3] 5   10 [25] 15   4 [_____] 6

■ Underline the **two** words, one from each group, that are most **opposite** in meaning.

Example (friendly, <u>enemy</u>, silent)   (<u>ally</u>, kind, whisper)

6. (brilliant, hour, immense)   (minute, detest, utilise)
7. (poisonous, liberty, popularity)   (captivity, capacity, secrecy)
8. (help, hesitate, holler)   (hexagon, hindrance, habit)
9. (entranced, transport, tranquil)   (adjust, agitated, turquoise)
10. (obstinate, obstacle, occupied)   (blockage, flexible, faded)

■ Change the first word into the last word. Only change **one** letter at a time, making two new words in the middle.

Example GILT [__SILT__][__SALT__] MALT

11. SLIP [_____][_____] FLAN   13. GRAIN [_____][_____] BRAWL
12. MILK [_____][_____] SALT   14. SLICE [_____][_____] GLADE

■ Circle the letter next to the **true** statement for each question.

15.   Nomadic people move from place to place to make a living. Bedouin tribes are nomadic.

If the above statements are true, which one of the following statements must also be true?
   A. Bedouin people ride on camels.
   B. Nomadic people live in tents.
   C. Bedouin people move from place to place.
   D. Tribes are always nomadic.

16.   The study of stars, planets and galaxies is called astronomy. Mr Singh is an astronomer.

If the above statements are true, which one of the following statements must also be true?
   A. Mr Singh writes horoscopes.
   B. Mr Singh studies stars, planets and galaxies.
   C. Astronomers use telescopes.
   D. Astrologists build space rockets.

End of test.

Score:		Time taken:		Target met?	

■ Underline the word in the first group that goes best with the words in brackets.

Example <u>blue</u>, red, orange   (turquoise, navy, cyan)

1. misery, mentality, emotional   (jealousy, melancholy, ecstasy)
2. mountainous, canyon, peak   (crevasse, crevice, abyss)
3. lynx, toucan, trout   (heron, flamingo, pelican)
4. meteorite, meteorology, astronomer   (asteroid, meteor, satellite)
5. knowledge, thesaurus, synonym   (almanac, encyclopaedia, dictionary)

■ Underline the two words, **one** from each group, that best complete the sentence.

Example **Earth** is to (mud, dirty, <u>planet</u>) as **cow** is to (field, <u>mammal</u>, bull).

6. **Vertical** is to (upwards, axis, measured) as **horizontal** is to (degrees, sideways, downwards).
7. **Gold** is to (luminous, valuable, jewellery) as **tin** is to (inexpensive, unworthy, useless).
8. **Avert** is to (challenge, worship, avoid) as **grotesque** is to (disgusting, unimpressive, elegant).
9. **Factual** is to (documentary, pretentious, fictitious) as **persuade** is to (discuss, dissuade, disuse).
10. **Notorious** is to (infamous, remarkable, hazardous) as **expose** is to (situation, uncover, impose).

■ Make a new word by changing the first word of the third pair in the same way as the other pairs. Write the new word on the line.

Example lantern, ant   loneliest, one   marching, _____arc_____   (take the 2nd, 3rd, 4th letters)

11. striped, trip   cleaner, lean   closest, _____
12. tallow, low   window, now   marrow, _____
13. meals, slam   plots, stop   think, _____
14. fallow, fowl   turner, tern   bussed, _____

■ Work out the answers. Write your answers on the lines.

15. If the year 2000 was a leap year, how many leap years will there be altogether in the 21st century? _____

16. Zygus is on holiday in San Francisco. He catches the 8.55 a.m. tram from outside his hotel into the city centre. He alights 15 minutes later. Zygus then spends 3 hours sightseeing before going into a nearby restaurant where he has lunch for $1\frac{1}{2}$ hours. Following lunch, Zygus spends 2.5 hours shopping before catching another tram back to his hotel, 15 minutes away. What time does Zygus arrive back at his hotel? _____

End of test.

Score:		Time taken:		Target met?	

Use the information given to answer each sum. Write your answer as a **letter**.

Example A = 10   B = 6   C = 3   D = 12   E = 18   **B × C =** ___E___   (6 × 3 = 18)

1. A = 108   B = 96   C = 2   D = 10   E = 117   **D² + C³ =** _____

2. A = 60   B = 10   C = 3600   D = 6   E = 360   **B × D × A =** _____

3. A = 27   B = 9   C = 2   D = 6   E = 8   **(A × C) ÷ D =** _____

4. A = 4   B = 3   C = 2   D = 0   E = 1   **$^C/_A - ^E/_C$ =** _____

5. A = 50   B = 99   C = 17   D = 3   E = 53   **B ÷ D + C =** _____

In each group, three words go together and two are the odd ones out. Underline the two words that do **not** go with the other three.

Example <u>define</u>   certain   sure   <u>give</u>   definite

6. satin   cashmere   jumper   silk   shirt

7. harmony   clamour   tranquillity   uproar   pandemonium

8. entrance   exit   bewitch   captivate   upstairs

9. mercury   earth   magnesium   aluminium   ground

10. reckless   benevolent   kind   spiteful   compassionate

Using the alphabet to help you, find the letter pair that completes each sentence. Write it on the line.

A B C D E F G H I J K L M N O P Q R S T U V W X Y Z

Example **FG** is to **EF** as **LM** is to ___KL___.   (–1, –1)

11. **UG** is to **BK** as **SF** is to _____.

12. **RK** is to **LN** as **IX** is to _____.

13. **UO** is to **FL** as **HV** is to _____.

14. **TZ** is to **VT** as **DM** is to _____.

Work out the answers. Write your answers on the lines.

15. Zara did a survey about people's favourite sport. She found that 16% of people said swimming was their favourite sport and 46% of people said football. The remaining people said rugby was their favourite sport. What percentage of people said rugby was their favourite sport? _____

16. Tom works at a restaurant 6 days a week. On Monday and Tuesday he works 4 hours, and on Wednesday and Thursday he works 8 hours. The rest of the days he works 10-hour shifts. How many hours does he work in one week? _____

End of test.

Score:		Time taken:		Target met?	

Target time: **10 minutes**

■ Underline the two words, **one** from each group, that best complete the sentence.

Example **Earth** is to (mud, dirty, <u>planet</u>) as **cow** is to (field, <u>mammal</u>, bull).

1. **Incomprehensible** is to (illegitimate, illegible, understandable) as **malfunctioning** is to (malicious, operational, especial).

2. **Page** is to (paper, book, consort) as **shelf** is to (bookcase, drawer, ornament).

3. **Allege** is to (clamber, hilltop, claim) as **forsake** is to (pray, abandon, accompany).

4. **Uniform** is to (standard, multiple, clothing) as **rancid** is to (rotten, sumptuous, appealing).

5. **Hundred** is to (millennium, century, ancient) as **ten** is to (decayed, decade, decide).

■ Find the missing number in each sequence and write it on the line.

Example 7   14   ___21___   28   35   42   (+7 each time)

6. 70   61   52   43   _____   25

7. 4   8   16   32   _____   128

8. 36   9   36   _____   36   9

9. 57   56   58   57   _____   58

10. 7   27   47   67   _____   107

■ Find **one** missing letter that completes **both** pairs of words. Write it on the lines.

Example strea [_m_] ile   doo [_m_] arry

11. smel [___] ease   hal [___] rouble

12. vide [___] val   mang [___] nion

13. appl [___] arn   salt [___] ank

14. vira [___] ounge   spraw [___] apse

■ Work out the answers. Write your answers on the lines.

15. Joe is reading a book. The book has **600** pages and Joe starts reading on Monday. By Wednesday, he has read half the pages and on Thursday he reads **100** more. By Friday he has finished the book. His friend Charlie takes **6** more days to read the same book but Mustafa reads it in half Charlie's time. How many pages had Joe read by Thursday bedtime? _____

16. Natalie loves to paint her nails. She has **20** different pots of nail polish. Half of them are shades of pink, **3** of them are blue, **4** are green and the rest are red. Her friend, Leila, brings round her collection of nail polish. She has half the number that Natalie has: **3** of her pots are shades of pink, half are green and the rest are silver or gold. How many pots of polish are **not** red or blue? _____

End of test.

Score: _____   Time taken: _____   Target met? _____

Target time: 10 minutes

■ Find the missing number in each of these equations and write it on the line.

Example $20 - 5 = 12 +$ ___3___

1. $(12^3 - 28) \div 2 = 400 \times 2 +$ _____
2. $10(7 \times 9) = 8^2 \times 10 -$ _____
3. $186 \div 6 = 310 \div$ _____
4. $\frac{1}{2} \times 300 = \frac{1}{3} \times$ _____
5. $1^2 + 1 = 100 - 68 -$ _____

■ Underline the pair of words that are most **opposite** in meaning.

Example (lift, drop)   (snow, wind)   (listen, learn)

6. (apparent, imaginary)   (accidental, intentional)   (injurious, judgmental)
7. (summon, dismiss)   (muster, collect)   (dividend, divide)
8. (silence, solitude)   (impoverish, poor)   (luxury, squalor)
9. (fantasy, reality)   (metaphor, simile)   (terror, horror)
10. (tyrant, dictator)   (incompetent, capable)   (interior, introvert)

■ Match the number codes to the words. One code is missing. Use this to help you work out the answers to the questions. Write your answers on the lines.

WISH   HIDE   DISH   WIDE   2169   6172   4172

What is the code for:

11. **HEED**? _____   12. **SWEDE**? _____   13. **HISSED**? _____

14. What does the code **79967** mean? _____

■ Circle the letter next to the **true** statement for each question.

15. Carys plays the violin. The sound from a violin is produced by vibrating the strings with a bow.

If the above statements are true, which one of the following statements must also be true?
A. Carys plays the cello.
B. Carys plays in an orchestra.
C. Carys uses a bow to play her violin.
D. Violins are made from wood.

16. Pasteurisation is a process of heating milk to a high temperature so that it can be preserved for longer. The process kills bacteria in the milk that could be harmful to people.

If the above statements are true, which one of the following statements must also be true?
A. Milk evaporates when it is pasteurised.
B. It is safer for humans to drink pasteurised milk than unpasteurised milk.
C. Pasteurised milk is more expensive than unpasteurised milk.
D. Bacteria can cause colds.

End of test.

Score:		Time taken:		Target met?	

Schofield&Sims

the long-established educational publisher specialising in maths, English and science

Verbal Reasoning 6 is a collection of short, language-based problem solving tests. Each timed test includes age-appropriate questions, providing opportunities for children to practise and master verbal reasoning skills in preparation for the 11+ and other school selection tests. This book is part of the **Rapid Reasoning Tests** series and covers the following question types: word and letter patterns; vocabulary; spelling; number patterns and problem solving.

Rapid Reasoning Tests provides short, effective, timed tests in reasoning. The series comprises six books of verbal reasoning tests and six books of non-verbal reasoning tests.

Written by experienced teachers and designed for independent use, **Rapid Reasoning Tests** has been carefully structured to provide practice of key, standard format question types. Each collection of tests has been designed for use over one year and provides one section per term in order to support regular practice.

Key features

- **Short tests** requiring few resources that are easy to fit into a busy timetable.
- A **target time** for each test encourages children to work quickly and develop the necessary exam skills for success in the 11+ and other tests.
- **Pull-out answers** in the centre of each book can be easily removed.
- **Free downloads** to support the series are available from the Schofield & Sims website.

The full series includes the following books:

Verbal Reasoning 1 978 07217 1238 3	**Non-verbal Reasoning 1** 978 07217 1226 0	**(Ages 6–7)**
Verbal Reasoning 2 978 07217 1239 0	**Non-verbal Reasoning 2** 978 07217 1227 7	**(Ages 7–8)**
Verbal Reasoning 3 978 07217 1240 6	**Non-verbal Reasoning 3** 978 07217 1228 4	**(Ages 8–9)**
Verbal Reasoning 4 978 07217 1241 3	**Non-verbal Reasoning 4** 978 07217 1229 1	**(Ages 9–10)**
Verbal Reasoning 5 978 07217 1242 0	**Non-verbal Reasoning 5** 978 07217 1230 7	**(Ages 10–11)**
Verbal Reasoning 6 978 07217 1243 7	**Non-verbal Reasoning 6** 978 07217 1231 4	**(Ages 11–12)**

ISBN 978-07217-1243-7

9 780721 712437

ISBN 978 07217 1243 7
Key Stage 2
Age range 11–12

£3.95
(Retail price)

For further information and to place an order visit
www.schofieldandsims.co.uk or telephone 01484 607080